HAND in HAND

AUTHORS

ELAINE MEI AOKI • VIRGINIA ARNOLD • JAMES FLOOD • JAMES V. HOFFMAN • DIANE LAPP

MIRIAM MARTINEZ • ANNEMARIE SULLIVAN PALINCSAR • MICHAEL PRIESTLEY • CARL B. SMITH

WILLIAM H. TEALE • JOSEFINA VILLAMIL TINAJERO • ARNOLD W. WEBB • KAREN D. WOOD

Macmillan McGraw-Hill

NEW YORK • FARMINGTON

Authors, Consultants, and Reviewers

MULTICULTURAL AND EDUCATIONAL
CONSULTANTS

Alma Flor Ada, Yvonne Beamer, Joyce Buckner,
Helen Gillotte, Cheryl Hudson, Narcita Medina,
Lorraine Monroe, James R. Murphy, Sylvia Peña,
Joseph B. Rubin, Ramon Santiago, Cliff Trafzer,
Hai Tran, Esther Lee Yao

LITERATURE CONSULTANTS

Ashley Bryan, Joan I. Glazer, Paul Janeczko,
Margaret H. Lippert

INTERNATIONAL CONSULTANTS

Edward B. Adams, Barbara Johnson,
Raymond L. Marshall

MUSIC AND AUDIO CONSULTANTS

John Farrell, Marilyn C. Davidson,
Vincent Lawrence, Sarah Pirtle, Susan R. Synder,
Rick and Deborah Witkowski, Eastern Sky Media
Services, Inc.

TEACHER REVIEWERS

Terry Baker, Jane Bauer, James Bedi, Nora Bickel,
Vernell Bowen, Donald Cason, Jean Chaney,
Carolyn Clark, Alan Cox, Kathryn DesCarpentrie,
Carol L. Ellis, Roberta Gale, Brenda Huffman,
Erma Inscore, Sharon Kidwell, Elizabeth Love,
Isabel Marcus, Elaine McCraney, Michelle Moraros,
Earlene Parr, Dr. Richard Potts, Jeanette Pulliam,
Michael Rubin, Henrietta Sakamaki,
Kathleen Cultron Sanders, Belinda Snow,
Dr. Jayne Steubing, Margaret Mary Sulentic,
Barbara Tate, Seretta Vincent,
Willard Waite, Barbara Wilson, Veronica York

Macmillan/McGraw-Hill

A Division of The McGraw·Hill Companies

Macmillan/McGraw-Hill
1221 Avenue of the Americas
New York, New York 10020

Printed in the United States of America

ISBN 0-02-181127-X / 2, L.7, U.2
1 2 3 4 5 6 7 8 9 WEB 02 01 00 99 98 97 96

Hand in Hand

Contents

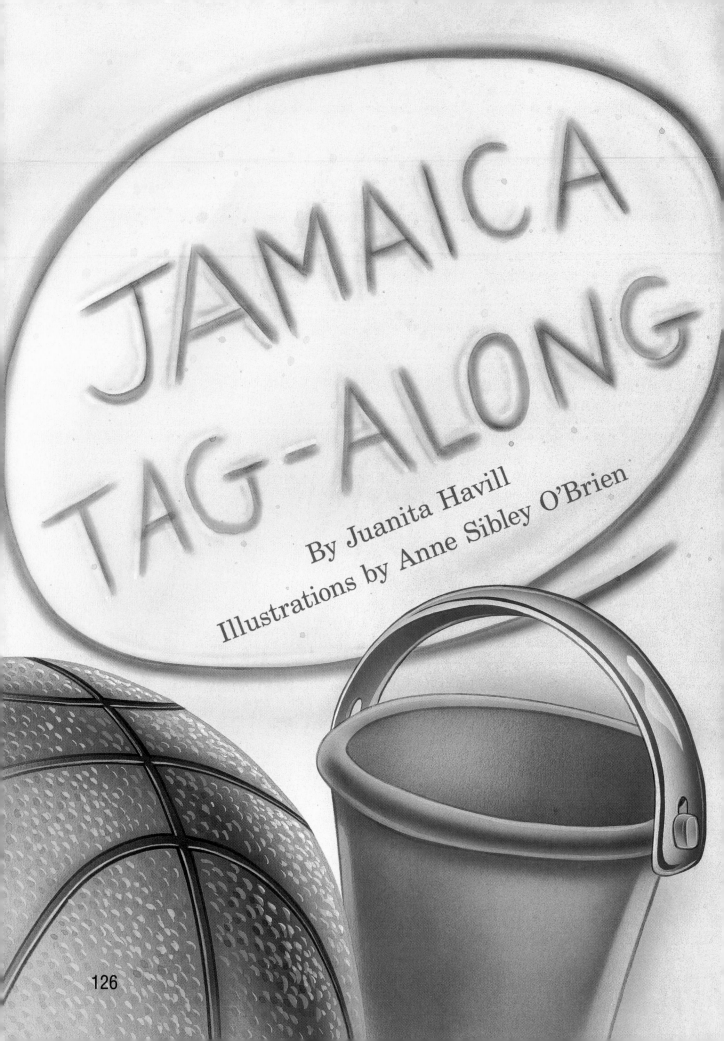

JAMAICA TAG-ALONG

By Juanita Havill

Illustrations by Anne Sibley O'Brien

Jamaica ran to the kitchen to answer the phone.
But her brother got there first.

"It's for me," Ossie said.

Jamaica stayed and listened to him talk.

"Sure," Ossie said. "I'll meet you at the court."

Ossie got his basketball from the closet. "I'm going to shoot baskets with Buzz."

"Can I come, too?" Jamaica said. "I don't have anything to do."

"Ah, Jamaica, call up your own friends."

"Everybody is busy today."

"I don't want you tagging along."

"I don't want to tag along," Jamaica said. "I just want to play basketball with you and Buzz."

"You're not old enough. We want to play serious ball."

129

Ossie dribbled his basketball down the sidewalk. Jamaica followed at a distance on her bike.

Buzz was already at the school court, shooting baskets with Jed and Maurice.

She parked her bike by the bushes and crept to the corner of the school building to watch.

That's not fair, Jamaica thought. Maurice is
shorter than I am.

Pom, pa-pom, pa-pom, pom, pom.
The boys started playing, Ossie and Jed against
Buzz and Maurice.

Jamaica sneaked to the edge of the court.

Maurice missed a shot and the ball came bouncing toward her. Jamaica jumped. "I've got the ball," she yelled.

"Jamaica!" Ossie was so surprised he tripped over
Buzz. They both fell down.

Jamaica dribbled to the basket and tossed the ball.
It whirled around the rim and flew out.

"I almost made it," Jamaica shouted. "Can I be on your team, Ossie?"

"No. N-O, Jamaica. I told you not to tag along."

"It's not fair. You let Maurice play."

"We need two on a team. Why don't you go play
on the swings and stay out of the way?"

"I still think it's not fair." Jamaica walked slowly
over to the sandlot.

She started to swing, but a little boy kept walking in front of her. His mom should keep him out of the way, Jamaica thought.

She looked up and saw a woman pushing a baby
back and forth in a stroller.

Jamaica sat down in the sand and began to
dig. She made a big pile with the wet sand from
underneath. She scooped sand from the mound to
form a wall.

"Berto help," said the little boy. He sprinkled
dry sand on the walls.

"Don't," said Jamaica. "You'll just mess it up."
Jamaica turned her back.

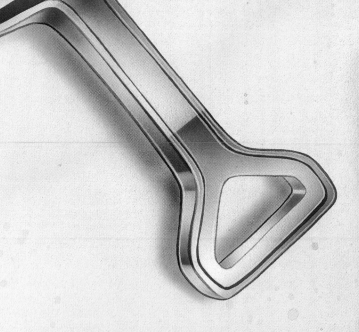

She piled the wet sand high.
She made a castle with towers.
She dug a ditch around the wall.

Jamaica turned to see if Berto
was still there. He stood watching.
Then he tried to step over the ditch,
and his foot smashed the wall.

"Stay away from my castle,"
Jamaica said.

"Berto," the woman pushing the
stroller said, "leave this girl alone.
Big kids don't like to be bothered
by little kids."

"That's what my brother always says," Jamaica
said. She started to repair the castle. Then she
thought, but I don't like my brother to say that.
It hurts my feelings.

Jamaica smoothed the wall. "See, Berto, like
that. You can help me make a bigger castle if
you're very careful."

Jamaica and Berto made a giant castle. They
put water from the drinking fountain in the moat.

"Wow," Ossie said when the game was over and the other boys went home. "Need some help?"

"If you want to," Jamaica said.

Jamaica, Berto, and Ossie worked together on the castle.

Jamaica didn't even mind if Ossie tagged along.

MEET JUANITA HAVILL

Juanita Havill has been telling stories for a long time. As a young child, Ms. Havill made up stories. Her stories were important to her. They let her make believe she could do all kinds of fun things. When she grew up, she became a teacher and visited many places. But she kept on writing. She took a writing class. She found that she liked to write for children. By now, she has written many children's books. Ms. Havill says, "I write to find out what I think, to give form to thought."

MEET ANNE SIBLEY O'BRIEN

Anne Sibley O'Brien was born in Chicago, Illinois. Most of her childhood was spent in Korea. She never forgot what it was like to live in another country. She learned about many other ways of life. Today Ms. O'Brien's art shows peoples of all colors. She has also drawn pictures for another book about Jamaica. In both books she worked hard to make the people seem real. She hoped to show how the members of Jamaica's family love each other.

HELPING KIDS

TAGALONGS

Dear Kids,
I have a big problem. I like to read. But every time I sit down to read, my little sister wants to play. If I don't play with my sister, she starts to cry. That's not all. My little sister follows me everywhere. Anytime I go to a friend's house, my sister wants to go too. Sometimes I just want to be alone. What should I do?

Suzi P.
Texas

We asked our Kids Helping Kids panel about Suzi's letter. Here are their ideas.

Meredith: Talk to your sister. Explain that you can't spend all your time with her.

Ranjit: Explain that you have some work to do, or that you've just finished your chores and would like some time to relax.

Jina: Ask your parents to talk to your sister. She may listen to your parents better than she will listen to you.

Tim: Sometimes when I have a friend over, my sister wants to play ball with us. We let her play for a while, then I show her another ball game she can play by herself. She gets so interested in her game that she forgets about us.

Thomasin: Invite one of her friends over to play with her. Then you can read or do whatever you want.

Matthew: I think you should play with your sister for a while when she asks you. There are other times when you can read, like after she goes to bed.

Meredith

Ranjit

Jina

Tim

Thomasin

Matthew

An umbrella and a raincoat
Are walking and talking together.

Buson

In the fields of spring,
The nightingales sing.
To gain their friendship,
The plum blossoms have burst open
In the garden of my house.

Anonymous

152

Laura's new this year in school.

She acts so opposite, it seems like a rule.

If someone says yes, Laura says no.

If someone says high, Laura says low.

If you say bottom, she'll say top.

If you say go, she'll always stop.

If you say short, Laura says tall.

If you say none, she says all.

If you say beginning, Laura says end. . .

But today she asked me to be her friend.

I said maybe

But not quite yes.

Then I said, "Want to take a walk?"

And Laura said, "I guess."

Jeff Moss

153

MEET
ELIZABETH WINTHROP

Elizabeth Winthrop wrote *The Best Friends Club* because of what happened to her as a child. She says, "I grew up with five brothers. Like Lizzie, I always made rules, but they paid no attention to me."

Ms. Winthrop thinks friendship is important to all children. She adds, "My children were always worried about having friends. How do I get a best friend? Will I keep her or him? What's a best friend like?"

She says about her writing, "When I write, I go into myself and find out what I'm feeling."

She adds, "I love writing for children. *The Best Friends Club* is a sequel to *Lizzie and Harold*. I knew their story wasn't over, so I wrote another one."

MEET MARTHA WESTON

Martha Weston was very excited about illustrating *The Best Friends Club* because she likes Lizzie so much.

She explains, "As a child, I was really bossy and had to show everyone how to do everything. Everything had to be done the way I wanted it to be done. Lizzie is like that, and I love her because she reminds me of myself.

"When I began drawing Lizzie and Harold, I asked my daughter and her friend to model for me. I asked them to do the things that Lizzie and Harold do in the story, and I took pictures of them. I paid them ten cents each for every picture I took."

THE BEST FRIENDS CLUB

BY ELIZABETH WINTHROP
ILLUSTRATED BY MARTHA WESTON

Lizzie and Harold were best friends.
Harold taught Lizzie how to do cat's cradle.
Lizzie taught Harold how to play running bases.

Lizzie shared her trick-or-treat candy with Harold, and Harold let Lizzie ride his big red bike.

They always walked home from school together.

"Let's start a best friends club," Lizzie said one day.

"Great," said Harold. "We can meet under your porch. That will be our clubhouse."

Harold painted the sign.

It said

THE BF CLUB.

"Now write *Members Only,*" said Lizzie.

"You write it," said Harold. "My teacher says my M's are too fat."

So Lizzie wrote *Members Only.*

"Who are the members?" Harold asked.

"You and me," said Lizzie.

"That's all?"

"Yes," said Lizzie. "You can be the president and I'll be the vice-president. The president gets to write down all the rules."

"You be the president," Harold said. "Your writing is better than mine."

"All right, then I'll be president," said Lizzie. "Now we'll make up the rules."

"Rule number one," said Harold. "The club meets under Lizzie's porch."

"Right," said Lizzie. "Rule number two. Nobody else can be in the club."

"Rule number three," said Harold. He thought for a long time. "I can't think of any more."

"Rule number three," said Lizzie. "Lizzie and Harold walk home from school together every day."

"Rule number four," said Harold. "Everybody in the club knows cat's cradle."

They heard voices. Someone was walking by. They could see two pairs of feet.

"It's Christina," whispered Lizzie. "She always wears those black party shoes."

"And Douglas," Harold whispered back. "His shoelaces are always untied."

"I'm only having Nancy and Amy and Stacey to my birthday party," they heard Christina say.

"My mother said I could have my whole class," Douglas answered. "We're going to play baseball."

"Oh goody," said Harold. "That means I'll be invited to Douglas's birthday party."

"I won't," Lizzie said gloomily. She was in a different class.

The next day, Harold came out of his classroom with Douglas.

"He wants to walk home with us," Harold said to Lizzie.

"He can't," said Lizzie.

"Why not?" asked Harold.

"Harold, remember the rules. We're best friends and we always walk home together," Lizzie said. "Just you and me."

"Oh yeah," said Harold. "I forgot."

Douglas looked very sad.

"Sorry, Douglas," Harold said. "See you tomorrow."

"Douglas's ears stick out," Lizzie said on the way home.

"So what?" said Harold.

"His shoelaces are always dripping," said Lizzie.

"I don't care about that," said Harold.

"I'll meet you in the clubhouse after snacks," said Lizzie.

"I can't come today," said Harold. "My mother wants me home."

Lizzie sat in the clubhouse all by herself.

She wrote down more rules.

They said

5. Best friends don't go to other people's birthday parties.

6. People with funny ears and drippy shoelaces are not allowed in the club.

The next day, Harold came out of his classroom with Douglas again.

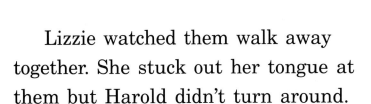

"Douglas asked me to play at his house," said Harold.

"*Harold,*" said Lizzie. "What about the club?"

"What club?" asked Douglas.

"None of your business," said Lizzie.

"I'll come tomorrow," said Harold. "I promise."

Lizzie watched them walk away together. She stuck out her tongue at them but Harold didn't turn around.

She went straight to the clubhouse and wrote down another rule. It said

7. Best friends don't go to other people's houses to play.

Then she threw a ball at the garage wall until suppertime.

"Douglas wants to be in the club," said Harold the next day.

"He can't be," said Lizzie. "Only best friends are allowed in this club."

She showed him all the new rules she had written down.

"This club is no fun," said Harold. "It has too many rules. I quit."

He crawled out from under the porch and walked home.

Lizzie took down his sign and put up a new one.

163

Douglas came down the street.

He was riding Harold's new bicycle.

Harold was chasing after him.

When Harold saw the sign, he stopped and read it.

"What does it say?" asked Douglas.

"It says, 'Lizzie's Club. Nobody Else Allowed,'"
Harold said.

Harold leaned over and looked at Lizzie. "You can't
have a club with only one person," he said.

"*I* can," said Lizzie.

"A three-person club is more fun," said Harold.
"Douglas knows how to do cat's cradle."
"But he's not a best friend,"
said Lizzie.

"It'll be a different kind of club," said Harold.
"We'll make up a new name."
"Maybe," said Lizzie.
She sat under the porch and watched them.
First they played bicycle tag.
Then they threw the ball at her garage wall.

"Want to play running bases?" Lizzie asked.

"I don't know how," said Douglas.

"I'll teach you," said Lizzie.

They took turns being the runner. Lizzie was the fastest.

Douglas whispered something to Harold.

"Douglas wants you to come to his birthday party," said Harold.

Then Lizzie whispered something to Harold.

"Lizzie says yes," Harold said to Douglas.

"And I've thought of a new name for the club," said
Lizzie. "Douglas can be in it too."

"Oh boy!" said Douglas.

"You can be the first member. I am the president
and Harold is the vice-president," said Lizzie.

"That's okay with me," said Harold.

"Me too," said Douglas.

It was getting dark.

Douglas went home for supper.

Lizzie crawled back under the porch. She tore up her sign and her list of rules.

"What's the new name for the club?" Harold asked.

"I'll show you," said Lizzie.

She sat down and wrote in great big letters
    THE NO RULES CLUB.

Harold smiled.

He stuck up the sign with a thumbtack.

Then they both went upstairs to Lizzie's house
for supper.

I'd like you for a friend.
I'd like to find the way
Of asking you to be my friend.
I don't know what to say.

What would you like to hear?
What is it I can do?
There has to be some word, some look
Connecting me to you.

MYRA COHN LIVINGSTON

174

DOWN THE WALK

We're racing, racing down the walk,
Over the pavement and round the block.
We rumble along till the sidewalk ends—
Felicia and I and half our friends.
Our hair flies backward. It's whish and whirr!
She roars at me and I shout at her
As past the porches and garden gates
We rattle and rock
On our roller skates.

Phyllis McGinley

OUR SOCCER LEAGUE

BY CHUCK SOLOMON

WE'RE THE FALCONS.
WE PLAY SOCCER!

Today the game is with our friends, the Sluggers. They wear blue shirts.

First everyone stretches.

Then we practice.

In soccer, you dribble the ball with your feet.

You pass to your teammates.

And you try to kick the ball through the goal, if you can.

Goalies need practice, too. They stop the other team from scoring, and they're the only players on the field who can touch the ball with their hands.

It's game time!

The coaches give us our positions for the opening kickoff.

The Sluggers kick off and burst downfield. They charge to the goal. There's a goal kick.

Defense! Our goalie, Toby, makes a save. Toby throws it out, and we have the ball.

Eric dribbles to midfield . . . with the Sluggers in pursuit. Eric passes . . .

but a Slugger intercepts! He gets his foot behind the ball . . . and boots it!

The Sluggers have the ball.

But then it is kicked out-of-bounds. Whenever a team puts the ball out, the other team throws it back in.

Moira throws it in for us.

"Don't use your hands, Johnny!"

Eric booms it.

Score! It's one to nothing, Falcons.

Teams	1st half	2nd half	Final
Falcons	1		
Sluggers			

But not for long.

The Sluggers bounce right back and tie the game.

It's now one to one.

Teams	1st half	2nd half	Final
Falcons	1		
Sluggers	1		

The score is still tied at one to one when the coaches call halftime.

Whew! It feels good to take a break.

After a ten-minute rest . . .

we're back to the game!

184

We charge down to the Slugger's goal.

Olivier's kick is wide . . .

and the Sluggers take the ball.

185

Here comes our defense
at midfield.

The two players collide.

It's anybody's ball.

The Sluggers and Falcons
battle for the ball.

The ball goes up . . .

Joely kicks it . . .

Oh, no! "Hand ball!" Since a Slugger touched the ball, we get a free kick.

Jonathan booms it and we have control again.

No one scored, and the clock is running out. Only five minutes are left in the game.

5:00

190

3:00

2:00

Out-of-bounds on a header.

193

Ted throws it in.

The Sluggers boot the ball
into the open field.

John's set . . . boom!

Score! It's two to one,
Sluggers!

195

We try our best to tie the score . . .

but the clock runs out.

196

0:00

Teams	1st half	2nd half	Final
Falcons	1	0	1
Sluggers	1	1	2

197

The Sluggers celebrate . . .

and we give ourselves a cheer.

When you play a great game . . .

everybody wins!

198

MEET CHUCK SOLOMON

"I wanted to write *Our Soccer League* because soccer is such a good sport for children," says Chuck Solomon. "Soccer doesn't require much equipment, it's not too rough, and running is good exercise. Besides, both girls and boys can play it together."

Mr. Solomon wrote this book to show children how to play soccer. He said, "I also wanted to show the excitement and feelings you get when you play the game.

"I photographed this book during an actual game, just as it happens in the book. As I was taking pictures, an editor was writing what was happening. After I developed the photographs, I wrote the story. It was important for me to tell the story just the way it happened."

TRUE BUT STRANGE

By Christina Wilsdon

Everything on these pages is true. Honest. We wouldn't kid you.

Sock-er?

Pele, one of the greatest soccer players in history, practiced his moves as a kid. He didn't have a soccer ball, so he used an odd "foot" ball: a sock full of rags!

Having a Ball

Usually only one soccer ball is used in a whole soccer game. But one pro football game can use up as many as 24 footballs. And a baseball game might use up 100 or more baseballs!

Bad Sports

King Edward II banned soccer in England about 650 years ago because the game was too noisy. Other kings banned soccer because they wanted people to spend more time learning how to use a bow and arrow!

World Pup

The team that wins the World Cup takes home a beautiful trophy. In 1966, someone stole this trophy. A dog named Pickles found it while digging in a garbage heap!

Town Ball

Soccer games in England 800 years ago were really big deals. Teams were made up of whole towns! A team could have more than 100 people.

BY KATHLEEN M. MULDOON
Illustrated by Linda Shute

Princess Pooh

My big sister is ten years old. Her name is Penelope Marie Piper, but everyone calls her Penny. Everyone except me. I, Patty Jean Piper, call her Princess Pooh. No one knows I call her that, but it's the perfect name for her. All day she just sits on her throne with wheels and tells everybody in the whole world what to do.

When we go shopping at the mall, Princess Pooh rides on her throne while Dad wheels her around. She smiles and waves like she's some kind of movie star. Mom carries the Princess's crutches and I, Patty Jean the Servant, carry packages. Sometimes there are so many I look like a box with legs.

Everyone loves the Princess. Grandma and Grandpop and all the aunts and uncles and cousins in our family hug her and say how sweet and wonderful she is. Then they look at me and say I am growing like a weed. That's the way it has been for a million years. The Princess is a flower. I, plain old Patty Jean, am a weed.

Once we went to a carnival. Princess Pooh watched me ride a hundred times on the roller coaster. It was fun, but it would have been better with a friend. I almost wished the Princess could ride with me. Then I tried to win a pink stuffed poodle. I spent all my allowance and threw a thousand balls, but I couldn't knock down the bottles. When we left, the man handed Princess Pooh a yellow stuffed poodle with a diamond collar! That's how it is. Everyone gives her things.

My school is a hundred years
old. It is so far from my house
I have to ride for hours on a
school bus to get there.
Princess Pooh goes to the
new school right across the
street. She can wheel
herself there in one
second.

If it rains, Dad
carries her and her
throne to his car and
gives her a one-second
ride. I, Patty Jean, wear
an icky yellow raincoat and
stand in mud puddles,
waiting for the bus.

Saturday is chore day. Mom mows the lawn. Dad washes clothes and cleans the garage. Then he brings the clean clothes to the Princess, and she folds them into piles on the table. I, Patty Jean the Maid, clean the bathroom.

One Saturday, Mom asked me to fold clothes because Princess Pooh had therapy. I sat at the table pretending I was the Princess. I folded the clothes very fast and put them in perfect stacks. When the Princess came home, I waited for Mom to tell her to clean the bathroom. But Mom put her right to bed because she was tired. So I, exhausted Patty Jean, had to clean the bathroom, too.

It is summer now. All my friends have gone to camp—everyone except me. Mom says there's no money to send me to camp because the Princess got new braces for her legs.

Princess Pooh doesn't need them anyway because all she does is sit. She only takes little tiny walks, like when she has to go to the bathroom at a restaurant and her wheelchair won't fit through the door. Mom says she walks at therapy, too, but I've never seen her do it.

After dinner I go outside. The Princess is in the hammock reading a book.

"Do you want to make a puppet show?" I ask.

"No, thanks," she says in her princess voice. "I'm going to read lots of books so I can win a prize in the summer reading program."

I don't feel like reading, but I get a book anyway and look at the pictures. I am finished in one minute.

"This book is boring," I say. "Let's play with puppets now." The Princess doesn't answer. I look over at the hammock—there she is, asleep.

Behind the tree is the throne. Seeing it empty gives me the best idea anyone in the whole world has ever had. Today I, Patty Jean, will be the Princess!

I sit on the throne. It is covered with cushions and feels like a cloud.

"I will rest on my golden throne for the whole evening," I say. I imagine all the people in my kingdom, looking at me and loving their beautiful new princess.

The throne is hard to wheel on the grass, so I get up and pull it to the front yard. "Now I will spend *every minute* on the throne," I say.

I decide to ride to the Princess's school. There is a nice, steep little hill on the grass near the sidewalk. Maybe it would be fun to ride down it. I sit down and give the throne a good, hard push.

PLOP! The throne dumps me out on the sidewalk and lands upside down on top of me. My knee has a tiny cut on it, but it doesn't hurt much. Still, I'm glad no one is around to laugh. I wonder if Princess Pooh ever fell when she was learning. I put the throne rightside up and get back on it. Then I ride to the corner. I go down the low place on the curb so I can cross the street.

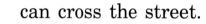

When the light turns green, I push the wheels as fast as I can. I make it to the island in the middle, but then the light turns red again.

Cars and trucks and buses rush by. I cover my face so I will not see myself go SPLAT.

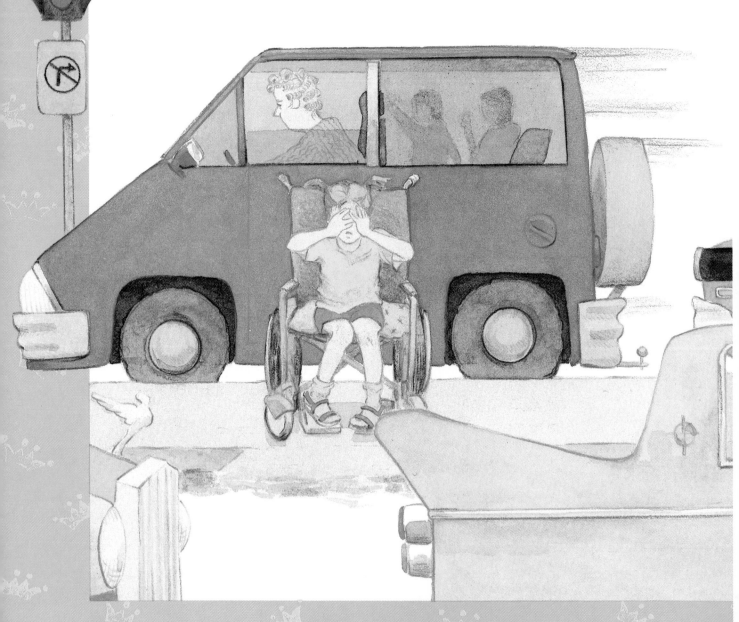

Finally, the traffic stops and the light is green again. I finish crossing the street. I push the throne up the low place at the crosswalk. It is hard to go uphill, but I do it. I wheel down the sidewalk. I've been pushing so hard I feel like both my arms are broken.

Some grown-ups are walking toward me. They look at me and my throne, and then they turn away fast, like I do when I'm watching a scary movie. Does this happen to Princess Pooh?

Some boys are playing on the sidewalk and will not move out of my way. "Why don't you go over me, Wheel Legs?" says one of them. All his friends laugh. "I'll beat you up!" I yell, but they just laugh some more and run away.

I see an ice-cream truck on the school playground. Lots of big kids are crowded around it. I make a shortcut across the baseball field, but by the time I get there and take some money out of my pocket, the worst thing in the world has happened. Great big raindrops have started falling over everything! SLAM goes the window on the truck. The children squeal and run away.

The man drives off and I'm alone on my wet throne.

The rain comes faster and faster. I think about running home, too, but I can't leave the throne out in the rain. Besides, I am still the Princess. I'm spending every minute on my throne, even if I do get wet! So I push harder and harder. When I get back to the baseball field, I can see it's a muddy mess. The wheels of the throne sink down, down, down. They stop turning. My hands are covered with mud. I jump off the throne, and my new sandals sink, too. My feet go with them. By the time I pull the throne out, I am wetter and colder than I have ever been in my whole life. I, Princess Patty Jean, am a royal mess. It is definitely time to quit sitting on the throne.

The rain stops. Across the street there is a rainbow. I notice Dad standing in our front yard. He is calling and calling, but the cars and trucks are so noisy I can't hear him. Mom is walking up the street, looking around. I drag the muddy throne across the rest of the field to the sidewalk.

Then I cross the street. When Mom sees me, she runs and holds out her arms. Dad is right behind her. "I didn't mean to mess up the throne. I'm sorry," I say.

"Throne?" says Mom. "Oh, the *wheelchair*. We thought you were lost!"

"You weren't looking for the chair?" I say.

"Patty Jean, we were looking for *you*." Mom hugs me some more. "You shouldn't have taken Penny's chair. But we're so glad you're back!"

Mom washes me in the bathtub and puts me to bed just like she does for Penny. After Dad and Mom say good-night and turn out the lights, I lie there thinking.

"Penny," I whisper. "Are you awake?"

"Uh-huh."

"Do you like walking better than sitting?"

"Well," she says, "walking makes me awful tired, but so does pushing my wheelchair.

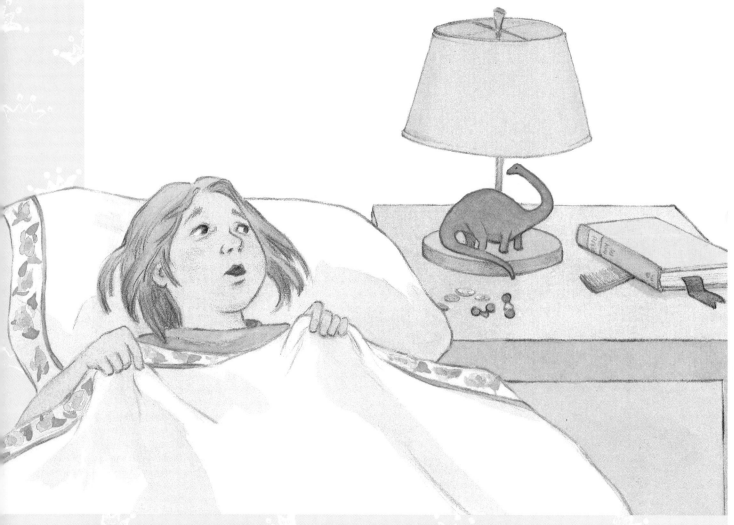

I guess I like the wheelchair best because I can do things with my hands while I sit. When I use my crutches, I can't."

"How can you smile all the time when you're in that yucky chair?"

"It's not yucky," says Penny. "It takes me places I can't go if I just have my crutches."

That makes me think some more. "I'm sorry I took your chair," I say.

"That's all right. Just go to sleep now."

But I'm wide awake. I lie there and wish
very hard that my sister will always be able
to do things that make her happy. I think
that maybe Princess isn't a good name for
her, after all. Maybe it's nicer that she's just
Penelope Marie and that I am her sister,
Patty Jean Piper.

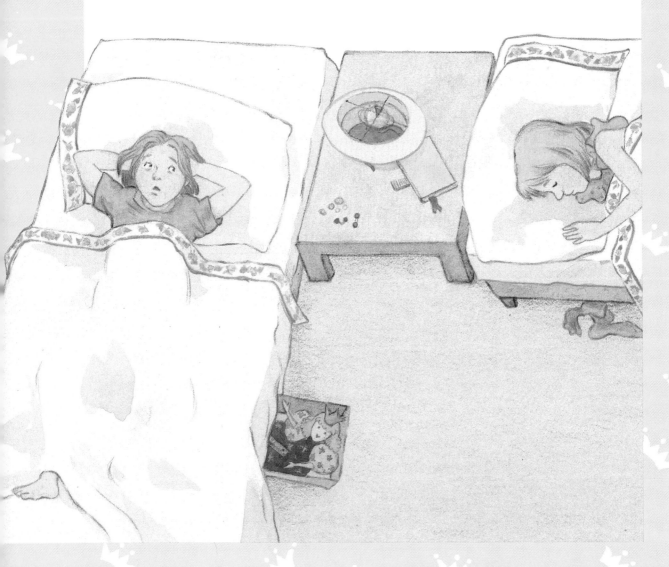

Meet

KATHLEEN M. MULDOON

Kathleen M. Muldoon knows what it is like to be physically challenged—on one leg, she wears a brace, and on the other, an artificial leg. Talking to children, she began to realize what it's like to be a brother or sister of someone like herself. She found that these children often get pushed aside because their brother or sister needs so much attention. So Ms. Muldoon decided to write a story from the sister's point of view.

Children ask Ms. Muldoon how she came up with the name "Princess Pooh." She says, "I thought of the name 'Princess Pooh' because *pooh* is a word children love to say and hear. It's like saying 'you're not so great,' so I thought it'd be a perfect nickname for the sister."

Meet
LINDA SHUTE

"What made me want to create the pictures for *Princess Pooh?* It was the voice of Patty Jean I heard speaking from the typewritten manuscript. She sounded like a spunky, funny, and thoughtful person I'd like to know. I felt the story is as much about being sisters as it is about using a wheelchair, and I tried to show that in my pictures."

Since Hanna Moved Away

The tires on my bike are flat.
The sky is grouchy gray.
At least it sure feels like that
Since Hanna moved away.

Chocolate ice cream tastes like prunes.
December's come to stay.
They've taken back the Mays and Junes
Since Hanna moved away.

Flowers smell like halibut.
Velvet feels like hay.
Every handsome dog's a mutt
Since Hanna moved away.

Nothing's fun to laugh about.
Nothing's fun to play.
They call me, but I won't come out
Since Hanna moved away.

JUDITH VIORST

227

DIAGRAMS

A Basketball Court

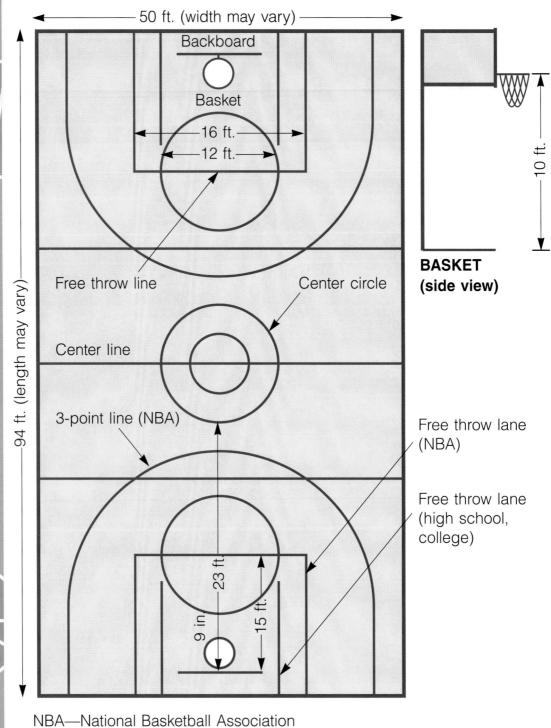

50 ft. (width may vary)

94 ft. (length may vary)

Backboard

Basket

16 ft.

12 ft.

Free throw line

Center circle

Center line

3-point line (NBA)

23 ft.

9 in

15 ft.

BASKET
(side view)

10 ft.

Free throw lane
(NBA)

Free throw lane
(high school,
college)

NBA—National Basketball Association

DIAGRAMS

How a Flood Forms

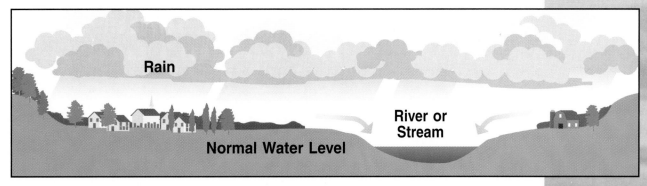

Rain

River or
Stream

Normal Water Level

1. Land Stage Water from rain or melted snow falls
to the land. After a while, the soil cannot hold any more
water. The water begins to move over the land.

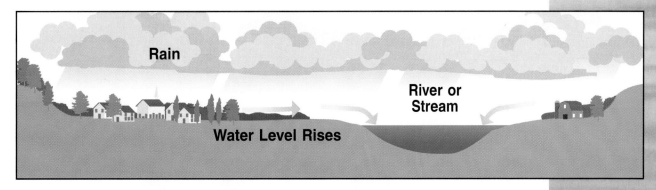

Rain

River or
Stream

Water Level Rises

2. Channel Stage The water from rain or melted snow
flows into a stream or river. The water begins to rise.
Water spills onto the land near the river.

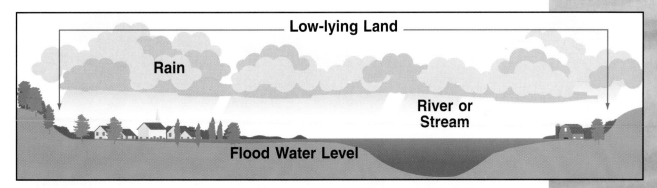

Low-lying Land

Rain

River or
Stream

Flood Water Level

3. Flood Stage Water spills over the banks of a stream
or river. The water then spreads across the low-lying
land near a stream or river.

Directions

PLAY NUMBER SPUD

Before Playing: Get a big, soft ball.
Count off so that everyone has a number.

1. One player throws the ball in the air and calls out a number. The others run away.

2. The player whose number was called catches the ball and yells "Freeze!"

3. The player with the ball throws it at the feet of any player close by.

4. The player whose feet are hit calls out **S** for the first letter in **SPUD**. The player then throws the ball in the air, calling out a new number.

5. Each time a player's feet are hit, he or she calls out the next letter of the word **SPUD**. When a player is hit four times and has spelled out **SPUD**, he or she is out.

The way-to-win choices:

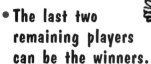

- The last two remaining players can be the winners.
- Any player who lasts for ten minutes or more is a winner.
- Invent your own ideas for winning.

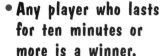

FORMS AND APPLICATIONS

Fun • Informative • Creative

SCIENCE & EARTH

A Magazine For Children

─── **ORDER FORM** ───

Please Print

NAME _ELIZABETH RILEY_

ADDRESS _431 TUPELO STREET_

CITY _PRESTON_ **STATE** _KANSAS_ **ZIP** _00000_

COUNTRY _U.S.A._

TELEPHONE (_9_/_1_/_3_) _5_ _5_ _5_ ─ _7_ _2_ _9_ _9_

DATE OF BIRTH _APRIL_ _4_ _1990_
                MONTH   DAY   YEAR

☐ 1 YEAR (8 ISSUES) $12.00
☑ 2 YEARS (16 ISSUES) $20.00

☑ PAYMENT ENCLOSED ☐ BILL ME

Elizabeth Riley
Signature

Ann Riley
Signature of Parent or Guardian
(Required if under 18)

DATE: _7_ / _4_ / _97_
     MONTH / DAY / YEAR

Return to: SCIENCE AND EARTH
               P.O. BOX 90
               MONTGOMERY, WA 00000

GRAPHS

Soccer Goals Scored This Season

Player	⚽ = 1 Goal
Abby	⚽ ⚽ ⚽ ⚽ ⚽ ⚽ ⚽ ⚽ ⚽ ⚽ ⚽
Eric	⚽ ⚽ ⚽ ⚽
Joan	⚽ ⚽ ⚽ ⚽ ⚽ ⚽
Jonathan	⚽ ⚽ ⚽
Moira	⚽ ⚽ ⚽ ⚽ ⚽ ⚽ ⚽ ⚽ ⚽
Toby	⚽ ⚽ ⚽ ⚽ ⚽ ⚽ ⚽

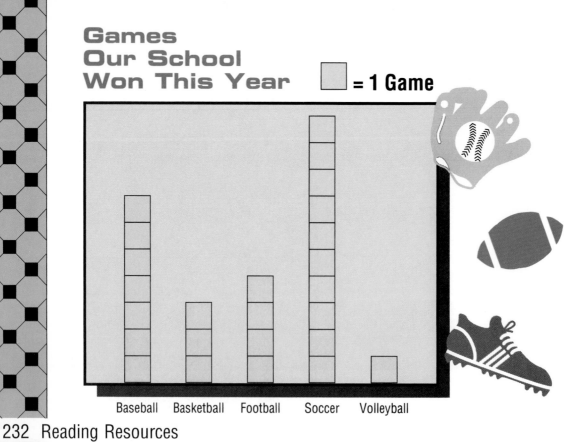

Games Our School Won This Year ☐ = 1 Game

Baseball   Basketball   Football   Soccer   Volleyball

MAPS

WEATHER MAP: UNITED STATES

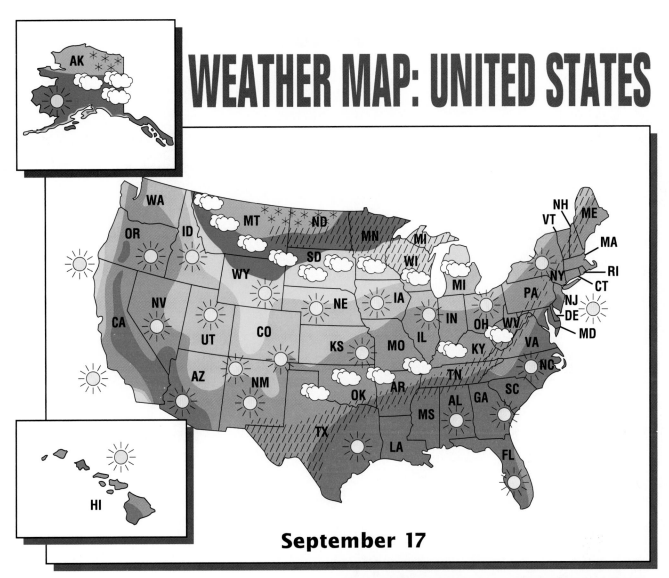

September 17

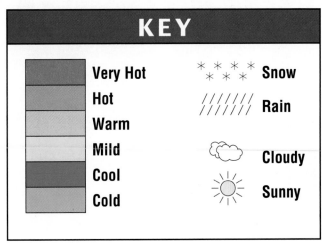

MAPS

Long Meadow Park

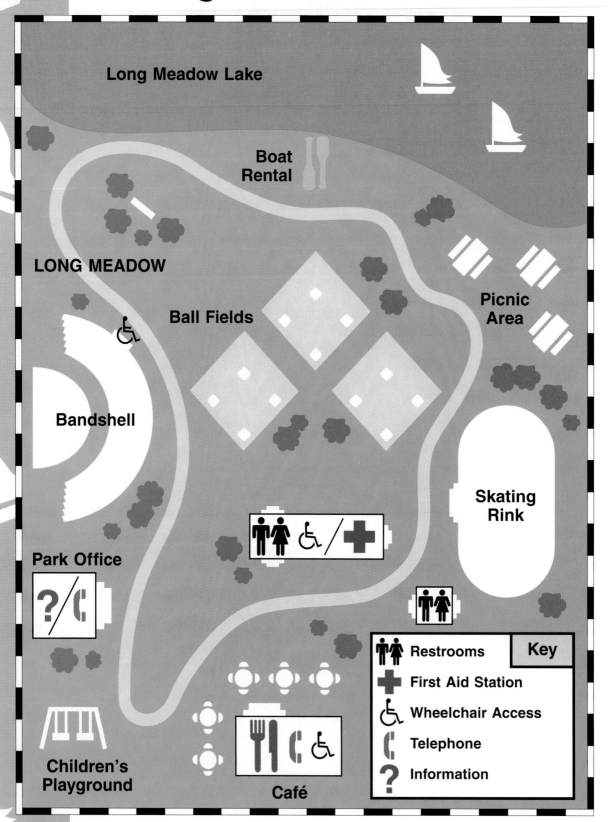

Long Meadow Lake

Boat Rental

LONG MEADOW

Ball Fields

Picnic Area

Bandshell

Skating Rink

Park Office

Children's Playground

Café

Key

Restrooms

First Aid Station

Wheelchair Access

Telephone

Information

MAPS

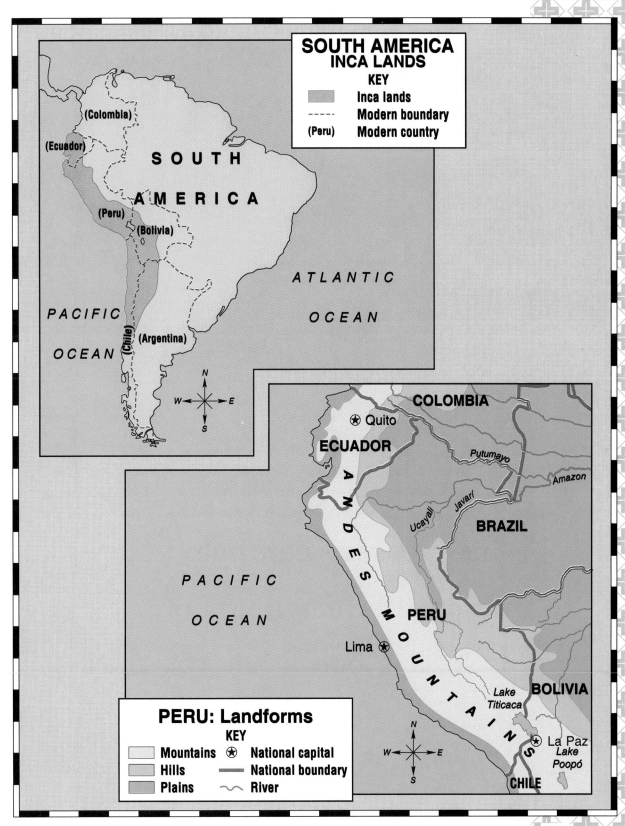

SOUTH AMERICA
INCA LANDS
KEY
- Inca lands
- ---- Modern boundary
- (Peru) Modern country

SOUTH

AMERICA

(Colombia)

(Ecuador)

(Peru)

(Bolivia)

ATLANTIC

OCEAN

PACIFIC

OCEAN

(Chile) (Argentina)

N W E S

PACIFIC

OCEAN

COLOMBIA

Quito

ECUADOR

Putumayo

Amazon

Ucayali

Javari

BRAZIL

ANDES MOUNTAINS

PERU

Lima

Lake Titicaca

BOLIVIA

La Paz

Lake Poopó

CHILE

N W E S

PERU: Landforms
KEY
- Mountains   ⊛ National capital
- Hills   — National boundary
- Plains   ∿ River

GLOS

This glossary can help you to find out the meanings of words in this book that you may not know.

SARY

The words are listed in
alphabetical order. Guide words
at the top of each page tell you the
first and last words on the page.

Aa

allow

Allow means to give permission to or for. They do not **allow** ball playing on the beach. ▲ **allowed, allowing.**

ancient

When something is **ancient,** it is very old. Leslie wants to visit the **ancient** pyramids in Egypt during her vacation.

ancient

arrow

1. A symbol shaped like an **arrow,** that points the way to something. The **arrow** on the sign shows the way to the beach.
2. An **arrow** is a thin stick that has a point at one end and feathers at the other. An **arrow** can be shot from a bow. ▲ **arrows.**

Bb

beach

A **beach** is a rocky or sandy strip of land that is close to a lake or an ocean. The **beach** is covered with sand. ▲ **beaches.**

bottle

A **bottle** is something that is used to hold liquids. A **bottle** may be made of glass or plastic. ▲ **bottles.**

bought

Bought comes from the word **buy.** I **bought** Pam a book for her birthday.

bounce

Bounce means to move back after hitting something. Cal threw the ball and watched it **bounce** off the sidewalk.
▲ **bounced, bouncing.**

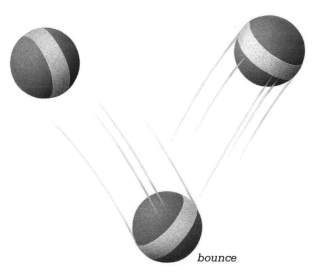

bounce

brace

A **brace** is something that holds parts together or keeps a thing from shaking. Andy wore a metal **brace** on his leg to help him walk. ▲ **braces.**

brave

If you are **brave,** it means that you are not afraid. The **brave** man climbed up the tall tree to get the kitten down safely.
▲ **braver, bravest.**

break

When something **breaks,** it divides into pieces. If you drop that mirror on the floor, it will **break.**
▲ **broke, broken, breaking.**

breeze

A **breeze** is a soft, gentle wind. The ocean **breeze** made us feel cool.
▲ **breezes.**

buy

When you **buy** something, it means you pay money for it. My grandmother sent us to the supermarket to **buy** orange juice.
▲ **bought, buying.**

G3

Cc

chance

Chance means that something might happen. There is a **chance** that it may snow tomorrow. ▲ **chances**.

charge

Charge means to rush at something. The angry bull started to **charge** the farmer.

charge

chase

Chase means to run after something and try to catch it. My dog likes to **chase** the car down the road. ▲ **chased, chasing**.

club

A **club** is a group of people who meet together for fun or some special purpose. Our book **club** will meet next Friday. ▲ **clubs**.

cover

To **cover** means to put something over or on something else. **Cover** the baby with a blanket so she won't get cold. ▲ **covered, covering**.

crawl

Crawl means to move slowly on your hands and knees. The baby is just beginning to learn how to crawl. ▲ **crawled, crawling**.

creek

A **creek** is a small stream. Josie's father taught her how to fish in a **creek**. ▲ **creeks**.

Dd

danger

Danger is anything that could cause harm or injury to you. The fire alarm sounded to warn people of the **danger.** ▲ **dangers.**

driver

A person who controls and steers a car, train, truck, or bus is a **driver.** The bus **driver** turned left onto Elm Street. ▲ **drivers.**

driver

during

During means at the same time as something else. Please try not to talk **during** the concert.

Ee

edge

An **edge** is the line or place where something ends. The dime rolled off the **edge** of the table. ▲ **edges.**

enemy

An **enemy** is a person, or group of people, who hates someone else. The cruel king was the **enemy** of his subjects. ▲ **enemies.**

enough

Enough means that there is as much of something as you need. There was **enough** food for everyone.

except

Except means that something or someone has not been included. Everyone **except** Joe was at the party.

expect

Expect means to think that something will happen. We **expect** fifty people to come to the family picnic on Sunday. ▲ **expected, expecting.**

fair

A **fair** is a place where people show and sell things they have grown or made. Benito won first prize for his pet pig at the state **fair.** ▲ **fairs.**

field

A **field** is an area of land where some games are played. Football is played on a **field.** ▲ **fields.**

float

To **float** means to rest on top of water or other liquid. We watched the leaf **float** down the stream. ▲ **floated, floating.**

float

flood

Flood means to cover with water. Did Jim **flood** the kitchen floor with water when he did the dishes? ▲ **flooded, flooding.**

footprint

A **footprint** is a mark made by a foot or shoe. We could see a **footprint** in the wet sand.

▲ **footprints.**

fountain

A **fountain** is a stream of water that shoots up into the air. José drank from the water **fountain.**

▲ **fountains.**

fountain

frighten

Frighten means to make a person or an animal afraid or scared. The cat tried to **frighten** the birds away.

▲ **frightened, frightening.**

Gg

gather

Gather means to collect or bring things or people together. We will all **gather** in the park tomorrow night to watch the fireworks.

▲ **gathered, gathering.**

Hh

hope

Hope means to want something very much. We **hope** that tomorrow will be a warm and sunny day so we can have a picnic at the beach.

▲ **hoped, hoping.**

horn

A **horn** is something you push, squeeze, or blow to make a sound. Ben squeezed the **horn** on his bicycle so everyone would know he was coming.
▲ **horns.**

howl

To **howl** means to make a loud wailing cry. The wind **howls** through the old house during a storm.
▲ **howled, howling.**

huge

Huge means very, very big. An elephant is a **huge** animal.

huge

Kk

kinfolk

Kinfolk are a person's relatives or family. All of my **kinfolk** live in the same city.

Ll

language

The words we speak, read, and write are called **language.** The second **language** Bridgette learned was Spanish.
▲ **languages.**

listen

Listen means to try to hear in a careful way. The children liked to **listen** to the story. ▲ **listened, listening.**

lock

A **lock** is a special part of a waterway or canal that ships use to go from one body of water to another. The ship was in the **lock,** waiting to enter the bay. ▲ **locks.**

Mm

meadow

A **meadow** is a field of grassy land. A **meadow** is often used for growing hay or as a pasture for animals. ▲ **meadows.**

member

When you belong to a group, you are a **member** of it. Even though it is a very large animal, the lion is a **member** of the cat family. ▲ **members.**

message

A **message** is information sent from one person to another. Mom called and left a **message** that she would be late. ▲ **messages.**

mountain

1. A large pile of things can be called a mountain. We had a **mountain** of laundry to wash on Saturday.

2. A **mountain** is a very high area of land. The **mountain** was high, and very hard to climb. ▲ **mountains.**

mountain

muddy

When something is **muddy** it is covered in wet dirt. Ken's boots were **muddy** after running through the woods. ▲ **muddier, muddiest.**

Nn

neighbor

A **neighbor** is someone who lives near you. Our **neighbor** cared for our dog when we went on vacation. ▲ **neighbors.**

Pp

pass

Pass means to move something from one person to another. Please **pass** the cereal to me. ▲ **passed, passing.**

peek

Peek means to look at something quickly or without anyone knowing. The squirrels **peek** out from behind the tree. ▲ **peeked, peeking.**

perfect

When something is **perfect,** it means that nothing is wrong with it. Jane's math test was **perfect.**

piano

A **piano** is a large musical instrument that has black and white keys. Ian practices the **piano** every day. ▲ **pianos.**

piano

pile

A **pile** is a lot of things lying on top of each other. We put all our old newspapers and magazines in a **pile** by the door. ▲ **piles.**

plain

A **plain** is an area of flat or almost flat land. As we drove across the **plain** we could see for miles. ▲ **plains.**

pocket

A **pocket** is a place to hold things that is sewn into clothing, bags, or suitcases. Barbara put her gloves in one **pocket** and her keys in another **pocket.** ▲ **pockets.**

point

Point means a certain moment in time. Jerry reached the **point** where he was so tired that he fell asleep. ▲ **points.**

porch

A **porch** is a part of a house that is outdoors. We sit on our **porch** in the summer because it is cool there. ▲ **porches.**

porch

prize

A **prize** is something that is won for doing very well in a contest or game. Janice's painting won first **prize** at the art show. ▲ **prizes.**

promise

To **promise** means to say that you will be sure to do something. Lionel made a **promise** not to tell my secret to anyone. ▲ **promised, promising.**

Qq

quit

Quit means to stop doing something. Joe **quit** swimming when he got cold. ▲ **quit, quitting.**

Rr

radio

A **radio** is a machine that you can turn on to listen to music, news, or other programs. Some evenings we listen to music on our **radio.** ▲ **radios.**

rage

Rage means to act or move with great force or violence. The weatherman watched the storm **rage** along the coast. ▲ **raged, raging.**

repair

Repair means to fix or mend something in order to put it into good condition again. Will she **repair** the broken leg of the table today? ▲ **repaired, repairing.**

repair

river

A **river** is water that is always moving from high ground to low ground. A **river** ends when it comes to another **river,** a lake, a sea, or an ocean. ▲ **rivers.**

rough

1. Something that is **rough** feels full of bumps. The bark of a tree feels **rough.**
2. Rough also means not gentle. The ocean was **rough** during the terrible storm. ▲ **rougher, roughest.**

rule

A **rule** tells you what you can do and what you cannot do. One **rule** at school is that you cannot run in the hallways.
▲ **rules.**

Ss

sail

Sail means to move over water. The children liked to **sail** their toy boats on the pond. ▲ **sailed, sailing.**

sand

Sand is a kind of earth that is made of tiny pieces of rock. There is **sand** on beaches and in deserts.

sand

score

1. A **score** is the number of points or the record of points made in a game or on a test. The final **score** was 5 to 4. ▲ **scores.**
2. When you make a point or points in a game or test, you **score** points. Rick **scored** two goals in the soccer game yesterday. ▲ **scored, scoring.**

serious

When you are **serious**, you are not silly or joking. The doctor was **serious** when he spoke to my mom

ship

A **ship** is a large boat that travels across deep water. There is a **ship** in the harbor. ▲ **ships.**

ship

shoulder

Your **shoulder** is the top part of your arm where it joins your body. I ripped my sweater at the shoulder. ▲ **shoulders.**

sidewalk

A **sidewalk** is a path to walk on next to the street. I walked home on the **sidewalk.** ▲ **sidewalks**

slide

Slide means to move easily on something. Please **slide** the book across the table to me. ▲ **slid, sliding.**

smooth

If something is **smooth**, you do not feel any bumps on it when you touch it. The skin of the apple is very **smooth.** ▲ **smoother, smoothest.**

sneak

Sneak means to move or act in a secret or sly way. The children tried to **sneak** into the theater. ▲ **sneaked** or **snuck, sneaking.**

softly

When something is done **softly,** it is done in a quiet or gentle way. Mother spoke **softly** because my sister was sleeping. ▲ **softer, softest.**

solid

When something is **solid,** it is hard and has a shape. When we freeze water, it becomes **solid.**

splash

Splash means to throw water or some other liquid around. Stand back or the car will **splash** you.

▲ **splashed, splashing.**

stout

Stout means thick and heavy. The baseball player was strong and **stout.**

▲ **stouter, stoutest**

stranger

A **stranger** is a person you do not know. A **stranger** rang our doorbell. ▲ **strangers.**

stream

A **stream** is water that is moving. Everyone stared at the fish splashing in the **stream.** ▲ **streams.**

stretch

When you **stretch** something, you make it as long as it can be. I like to **stretch** my arms when I wake up in the morning.

▲ **stretched, stretching**

stretch

suppose

If you **suppose** something will happen, it means that you think it will happen. I **suppose** it will rain this afternoon. ▲ **supposed, supposing.**

G15

sweet

If a food is **sweet,** it tastes as if there is sugar in it. Ice cream and candy are **sweet.** ▲ **sweeter, sweetest.**

swing

When you **swing** something, you make it move back and forth through the air. Patricia likes to **swing** her arms when she walks.
▲ **swung, swinging.**

Tt

team

A **team** is a group of people who play a game together. There are twenty people on our school's football **team.**
▲ **teams**

thin

Thin means not fat. A horse has a long, **thin** face. ▲ **thinner, thinnest.**

throne

A **throne** is a big chair that a king or queen sits on during special occasions. The day the princess became queen, she sat on her **throne** for the first time. ▲ **thrones.**

throne

tide

Tide means the regular rise and fall of the water in the oceans caused by the pull of the sun and moon on the earth. High **tide** happens twice a day. ▲ **tides.**

tie

When a game ends in a **tie,** it means that both teams have the same score, so neither team wins or loses. My soccer game ended in a **tie.** ▲ **ties, tied.**

touch

Touch means to put your hand on something. Don't **touch** the hot stove. ▲ **touched, touching.**

travel

Travel means to go from one place to another. We will **travel** by car. ▲ **traveled, traveling.**

Uu

understand

When you **understand** something, you know what it means. Andy can **understand** both English and Spanish. ▲ **understood, understanding.**

Vv

valley

A **valley** is the low land between hills or mountains. The **valley** has a river flowing through it. ▲ **valleys.**

valley

village

A **village** is a small group of houses. A **village** is usually smaller than a town. We drove through a tiny **village** in the mountains. ▲ **villages.**

village

Ww

warn

When someone tells you ahead of time to watch out for something that may happen. Did you **warn** him that it might rain? ▲ **warned, warning.**

whisper

Whisper means to speak in a very quiet voice. The teacher asked the students to **whisper** when they shared their stories. ▲ **whispered, whispering.**

whistle

1. A **whistle** is something you blow into that makes a sound. The police officer blew a **whistle** and all the cars stopped. ▲ **whistles.**
2. When you **whistle,** you make a sound by pushing air out though your lips or teeth. My dog always comes when I **whistle.** ▲ **whistled, whistling.**

whole

When something is **whole,** it has no parts missing from it. Twelve eggs make up a **whole** dozen.

ACKNOWLEDGMENTS

The publisher gratefully acknowledges permission to reprint the following copyrighted material:

"And Then" by Prince Redcloud. Used by permission of Lee Bennett Hopkins for the author. All rights reserved.

"Angel Child, Dragon Child" from ANGEL CHILD, DRAGON CHILD with text by Michele Maria Surat and pictures by Vo-Dinh-Mai. Text copyright © 1983 by Carnival Press, Inc. Illustrations copyright © 1983 by Vo-Dinh Mai. Permission to reprint the art from Vo-Dinh-Mai. Published by arrangement with Raintree/Steck-Vaughn Publishers. All rights reserved.

"April Rain Song" from THE DREAM KEEPER by Langston Hughes. Copyright © 1932 by Alfred A. Knopf, Inc. and renewed 1960 by Langston Hughes. Reprinted by permission of the publisher.

"The Best Friends Club." This is the entire text and nineteen illustrations from THE BEST FRIENDS CLUB by Elizabeth Winthrop with illustrations by Martha Weston. Text copyright © 1989 by Elizabeth Winthrop. Illustrations copyright © 1989 by Martha Weston. Reprinted by permission of William Morrow and Company, Inc./Publishers, New York.

Text and art of "Best Wishes, Ed" from WINSTON, NEWTON, ELTON, AND ED by James Stevenson. Copyright © 1978 by James Stevenson. Reprinted by permission of Greenwillow Books, a division of William Morrow and Company, Inc.

"Colores de Caracol" ("The rainbow showing") from VERY VERY SHORT NATURE POEMS by Ernesto Galarza. Copyright © 1972 by Ernesto Galarza. Reprinted by permission of Mrs. Mae Galarza.

"Come a Tide" from COME A TIDE by George Ella Lyon, pictures by Stephen Gammell. Text Copyright © 1990 by George Ella Lyon. Illustrations © 1990 by Stephen Gammell. All rights reserved. Reprinted by Permission of Orchard Books, New York.

Cover illustration of COULD BE WORSE! by James Stevenson. Copyright © 1977 by James Stevenson. By permission of William Morrow & Company, Inc. Publishers, New York.

"A Curve in the River" from MORE STORIES JULIAN TELLS by Ann Cameron. Illustrated by Ann Strugnell. Text copyright © 1986 by Ann Strugnell. Reprinted by permission of HarperCollins Publishers.

"Dear Daddy ..." from DEAR DADDY by Philippe Dupasquier. Copyright © 1985 by Philippe Dupasquier. Reprinted with the permission of Simon & Schuster Books For Young Readers.

"Eletelephony" from TIRRA LIRRA: RHYMES OLD AND NEW by Laura E. Richards. Copyright 1930, 1932 by Laura E. Richards. Copyright © renewed 1960 by Hamilton Richards. By permission Little, Brown and Company.

"Finding a Way" by Myra Cohn Livingston reprinted with permission of Margaret K. McElderry Books, an imprint of Simon & Schuster Children's Publishing Division, from THERE WAS A PLACE AND OTHER POEMS by Myra Cohn Livingston. Copyright © 1988 by Myra Cohn Livingston.

"Ham Radio" by Kenny A. Chaffin, from U. S. KIDS, Vol. 5, No. 2, February 1992 issue. Copyright © 1992, by Children's Better Health Institute, Benjamin Franklin Literary and Medical Society, Incorporated. Reprinted by permission.

"It's Dark in Here" is the text and art of "It's Dark in Here" from WHERE THE SIDEWALK ENDS by Shel Silverstein. Copyright © 1974 by Evil Eye Music, Inc. Reprinted by permission of HarperCollins Publishers.

"Jamaica Tag-Along" by Juanita Havill, illustrations by Anne Sibley O'Brien. Text copyright © 1989 by Juanita Havill, Illustrations copyright by Anne Sibley O'Brien, published by Houghton Mifflin. Reprinted by permission.

The book cover of JAMAICA'S FRIEND by Juanita Havill, copyright © 1986 by Juanita Havill, published by Houghton Mifflin Company. Reprinted by permission.

The book cover of JAMAICA AND BRIANNA by Juanita Havill, copyright © 1993 by Juanita Havill, published by Houghton Mifflin Company. Reprinted by permission.

"Laura" from THE BUTTERFLY JAR by Jeff Moss. Copyright © 1989 by Jeff Moss. Used by permission of Bantam Books, a division of Bantam Doubleday Dell Publishing Group, Inc.

Cover illustration of LIZZIE AND HAROLD by Elizabeth Winthrop, illustrated by Martha Weston. Copyright © 1986 by Elizabeth Winthrop. By permission of Lothrop, Lee & Shepard, New York.

"Llama and the Great Flood." This is the entire work from LLAMA AND THE GREAT FLOOD: A FOLKTALE FROM PERU by Ellen Alexander.

Copyright © 1989 by Ellen Alexander. Reprinted by permission of HarperCollins Publishers.

"Our Soccer League" from OUR SOCCER LEAGUE by Chuck Solomon. Copyright © 1988 by Chuck Solomon. Reprinted by permission of Crown Publishers.

"Postcards from the Earth" Copyright 1992 Children's Television Workshop (New York, New York). All rights reserved.

"Princess Pooh" is the entire text from PRINCESS POOH by Kathleen M. Muldoon with illustrations by Linda Shute. Text copyright © 1989 by Kathleen M. Muldoon. Illustrations copyright © 1989 by Linda Shute. Originally published in hardcover by Albert Whitman & Company. All rights reserved. Used with permission.

"Puff...Flash...Bang!" by Gail Gibbons, copyright © 1993 by Gail Gibbons, published by William Morrow and Company. Reprinted by permission.

"River Winding" is the text of RIVER WINDING by Charlotte Zolotow. Copyright © 1970 by Charlotte Zolotow. Reprinted by permission of HarperCollins Publishers.

"Since Hanna Moved Away" by Judith Viorst. Reprinted with permission of Atheneum Books for Young Readers, an imprint of Simon & Schuster Children's Publishing Division, from IF I WERE IN CHARGE OF THE WORLD AND OTHER WORRIES by Judith Viorst. Copyright © 1981 by Judith Viorst.

Cover illustration from SONG AND DANCE MAN by Karen Ackerman. Illustrated by Stephen Gammell. Illustration copyright © 1988 by Stephen Gammell. Reprinted by permission of Alfred A. Knopf.

Cover illustration from THE STORIES JULIAN TELLS by Ann Cameron. Illustrated by Ann Strugnell. Illustrations copyright © 1981 by Ann Strugnell. Reprinted by permission of Pantheon Books, a division of Random House, Inc.

"The Sun, the Wind and the Rain" from THE SUN, THE WIND AND THE RAIN by Lisa Westberg Peters. Text copyright © 1988 by Lisa Westberg Peters. Illustration copyright © 1988 by Ted Rand. Reprinted by permission of Henry Holt and Co., Inc.

"Tagalongs" from U. S. KIDS, Vol. 2, No. 5, April 1989 issue. Coyright © 1989 by Field Publications. Reprinted by permission.

"There Was An Old Pig With a Pen" is the text and art for this selection from THE BOOK OF PIGERICKS; PIG LIMERICKS by Arnold Lobel. Copyright © 1983 by Arnold Lobel. Reprinted by permission of HarperCollins Publishers.

"The Tide in the River" by Eleanor Farjeon reprinted by permission of Harold Ober Associates, Incorporated. Copyright © 1920 by Eleanor Farjeon. Renewed 1948.

"True But Strange" Copyright 1994 Children's Television Network (New York, New York). All rights reserved.

"An umbrella and a raincoat" by Buson. Reprinted with permission of Simon & Schuster Books for Young Readers, an imprint of Simon & Schuster Children's Publishing Division, from DON'T TELL THE SCARECROW AND OTHER JAPANESE POEMS by Issa, et al. Copyright © 1969.

"Until I Saw the Sea" from I FEEL THE SAME WAY by Lilian Moore. Copyright © 1967 by Lilian Moore. Reprinted by permission of Marian Reiner for the author.

"Water" by Joan Bransfield Graham. Reprinted by permission.

"The Water-Go-Round" by Dennis Lee. Reprinted by permission.

"We're Racing, Racing Down the Walk" by Phyllis McGinley. Reprinted by permission.

Cover illustration of WHAT'S UNDER MY BED? by James Stevenson. Copyright © 1983 by James Stevenson. By permission of William Morrow & Company, Inc. Publishers, New York.

"Write About a Radish" Text from "Write About a Radish" from DOGS & DRAGONS, TREES & DREAMS by Karla Kuskin. This poem originally appeared in NEAR THE WINDOW TREE by Karla Kuskin. Copyright © 1975 by Karla Kuskin. Reprinted by permission of HarperCollins Publishers.

COVER DESIGN: Carbone Smolan Associates
COVER ILLUSTRATION: Etienne Delessert

DESIGN CREDITS
Carbone Smolan Associates, front matter, 124-125

Bill Smith Studio, 148-149, 200-201
Function Thru Form, Inc., 228-229, 230, 234
Notovitz Design Inc., 231-233, 235